Harold R Foster

Prince Valiant

COMPRISING PAGES 641 THROUGH 686

Young Geoffrey

FANTAGRAPHICS BOOKS

ABOUT THIS EDITION:

Produced in cooperation with the Danish publisher Interpresse and several other publishers around the world, this new edition of *PRINCE VALIANT* is intended to be the definitive compilation of Hal Foster's masterpiece.

In addition to this volume, Fantagraphics Books has in stock sixteen more collections of Foster's *Prince Valiant* work (Vols. 2-14, 29-31). Future releases will continue reprinting 1950s material; once the series has "caught up" with its earlier releases, those will be reprinted, or (if they are still in print) skipped in order to complete the collection with the final era (late 1960s through 1982, when Foster handed over the strip to John Cullen Murphy). The ultimate goal is to have all 40 volumes in print simultaneously, making available the entirety of Hal Foster's 45-year epic.

ABOUT THE PUBLISHER:

FANTAGRAPHICS BOOKS has dedicated itself to bringing readers the finest in comic book and comic strip material, both new and old. Its "classics" division includes the *The Complete E.C. Segar Popeye*, the *Complete Little Nemo in Slumberland* hardcover collection, and the upcoming *Complete Pogo*. Its "modern" division is responsible for such works as Yellow Kid Award-winner *Love and Rockets* by Los Bros. Hernandez, Peter Bagge's *Hate*, the American edition of Munoz and Sampayo's *Sinner*, and *The Complete R. Crumb Comics*. See the back cover for details.

PREVIOUS VOLUMES IN THIS SERIES:

PRINCE VALIANT, Volume 15
"Young Geoffrey"
comprising pages 641 (May 22, 1949) through 686 (March 19, 1950)
Published by Fantagraphics Books, 7563 Lake City Way NE, Seattle, WA 98115
Editorial Co-Ordinator: Carsten Søndergaard
Colored by Montse Serra of Bardon Art, S.A.
Cover inked by Mårdøn Smet and colored by Teddy Kristiansen
Fantagraphics Books staff: Kim & Mark Thompson
Copyright © 1991 King Features Syndicate, Inc., Bull's, Interpresse, & Fantagraphics Books, Inc.
Printed in Denmark
ISBN 1-56097-065-0
First printing: December, 1991

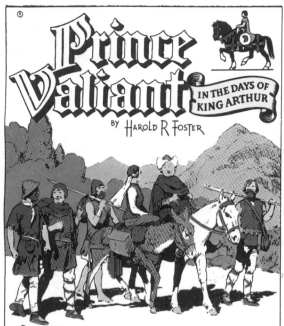

Prince Valiant

IN THE DAYS OF KING ARTHUR

BY HAROLD R FOSTER

Synopsis : WINNIE, THE WITCHWOMAN, AND OOM FOOYAT, THE GREAT WIZARD, TOUR THE FIEF AND GIVE ENTERTAINMENTS. EVERYONE HAS A JOLLY TIME AND PEOPLE COME FOR MILES AROUND TO SEE THEM.

OOM AMAZES THEM WITH HIS MAGIC, BUT JUST AS HE IS GOING GOOD SOMETHING ALWAYS CONTRIVES TO GIVE THE TRICK AWAY.

THE CLUMSINESS OF THE TWO SORCERERS AND THE TALES TOLD BY THEIR ESCORTS HAVE COMPLETELY DISCREDITED MAGIC AND THE PEOPLE WONDER WHY THEY EVER BELIEVED IN IT !

IT HAS BEEN A LONG TIME SINCE THE FRIGHTENED PEOPLE OF THIS FIEF HAVE LAUGHED, BUT HOW THEY LAUGH AT OOM ! AND POOR OOM! HOW HE HATES TO BE LAUGHED AT !

HE HAS SPENT ALL HIS LIFE TRYING TO BE A GREAT WIZARD..... ALL HAS BEEN SACRIFICED JUST TO HELP HIS FRIENDS. FOREVERMORE HE WILL BE RIDICULED, A CLOWN !

BUT THE RECRUITS ARE COMING IN NOW THAT OOM HAS REMOVED THEIR FEAR. FOR IT IS BETTER TO BE A WELL-FED SOLDIER THAN A POOR, LABORING SERF.

SMILING, BUT HEARTBROKEN, OOM FOOYAT, THE COMEDIAN, RETURNS TO lILLWYNDE TO FIND IT FULLY MANNED AND, FOR HIMSELF, A WARM AND FRIENDLY WELCOME !

"I STILL DON'T KNOW HOW YOU DID IT," SAYS SIR CADOR, "BUT YOU HAVE SAVED ME FROM A FOOLISH, HOTHEADED DUEL THAT MIGHT HAVE MEANT DISASTER. IT WILL TAKE YEARS TO THANK YOU ENOUGH ! "

OOM GOES HOME TO WINNIE, BRINGING A SUPPER GUEST. SOMEHOW THE LAUGHTER DOESN'T HURT ANY MORE ; NOT WHEN PEOPLE LAUGH WITH YOU, NOT AT YOU. HE IS CONTENT.

NEXT WEEK - *Amorous Delays*

641   5-22-49

Prince Valiant

IN THE DAYS OF KING ARTHUR

BY HAROLD R FOSTER

Synopsis: THE IMAGE OF GOLDEN ALETA AND PINK ARN IS EVER IN PRINCE VALIANT'S HEART; AND NOW, HIS QUEST COMPLETE, HE IS MORE THAN ANXIOUS TO RETURN TO THEM. THE FIRST DELAY IS CAUSED BY SIR CADOR, A BRAVE WARRIOR IN BATTLE, BUT A SIMPERING CLOWN IN THE PRESENCE OF GWYNN.

"HELP ME, VAL. I WISH TO TELL HER OF MY LOVE IN POETIC FASHION AS BECOMES A ROMANTIC SUITOR; BUT WHEN SHE IS NEAR I CAN ONLY MUMBLE LIKE A CLOD!"

VAL GOES STRAIGHTWAY TO GWYNN; "DO YOU LOVE SIR CADOR?" HE DEMANDS. HER CHIN COMES UP PROUDLY, "MY PERSONAL AFFAIRS ARE NONE OF YOUR BUSINESS, SIR VALIANT!"

THEN, BEFORE HIS FRIENDLY GRIN, HER ANGER MELTS. "YES, I DO, BUT THE BIG, HULKING DARLING IS TOO SHY TO TALK OF LOVE!" VAL TAKES HER BY THE ARM, "COME, WE WILL ATTEND TO THAT RIGHT NOW!"

"SIR CADOR! I HAVE WRITTEN A DECLARATION OF LOVE SUCH AS WOULD MELT THE HEART OF A STATUE! AND," HE ADDS, "TO GET OVER YOUR SHYNESS YOU CAN PRACTICE IT BEFORE GWYNN'S ARMOR!"

BUT VAL'S TOPLOFTY WORDS ARE TOO MUCH FOR SIR CADOR. "OH! GWYNN! GWYNN!" HE WHISPERS MISERABLY, "I LOVE YOU SO! WHY MUST I BE FOR-EVER DUMB IN YOUR PRESENCE?"

"AND WHY NOT, PRAY?" ANSWERS A TIMID VOICE, "MAYBE I LIKE YOU THAT WAY" AND THE JOB IS DONE

THEN VAL CALLS OSK, HIS SQUIRE, TO PREPARE FOR THE JOURNEY HOME. "BUT, SIRE," HE PRO-TESTS, "IT WILL TAKE SIX MONTHS TO MAKE SOLDIERS OF THESE RECRUITS...IT IS MY DUTY..."

© COPR 1949. KING FEATURES SYNDICATE Inc. WORLD RIGHTS RESERVED.

" AND AFTER THAT IT WILL TAKE THE REST OF MY LIFE TO TRAIN HELOISE. BETTER I STAY IN IILLWYNDE."

HAL FOSTER

NEXT WEEK - **And Now, Sir Gawain.**

642 5-29-49

Prince Valiant

IN THE DAYS OF KING ARTHUR
BY Harold R Foster

Synopsis: ONCE THE CASTLE OF IILLWYNDE WAS A HEALTHY PLACE OF DANGER AND HORROR; NOW IT IS POSITIVELY BILIOUS WITH LOVE. FIRST, OOM FOOYAT IS CHARMED BY 'WINNIE THE WITCH.' THEN SIR CADOR IS VANQUISHED BY THE FLUTTER OF AN EYELASH BELONGING TO GWYNN, AND FINALLY OSK GALLANTLY ALLOWS FAIR HELOISE TO CAPTURE HIM.

WITH GROWING FEAR, PRINCE VALIANT GOES IN SEARCH OF SIR GAWAIN. IT IS WORSE THAN HE FEARED! IN A CASTLE FILLED WITH WOMEN, SOME OF THEM COMELY, ALL OF THEM LONELY, SIR GAWAIN HAS BECOME A PET!

"RETURN TO CAMELOT!" HE LAUGHS, "WHY THE HASTE? I THINK I'LL DALLY HERE FOR A WHILE WHERE MY KNIGHTLY SERVICES ARE NEEDED."

"BUT YOU RUN ALONG, VAL. AFTER ALL, YOU ARE A FAMILY MAN NOW AND MUST REPORT HOME." VAL THINKS HARD FOR A MINUTE AND THEN – – –

"SPLENDID, GAWAIN! MEN ARE NEEDED IN THIS CASTLE WHERE THERE ARE SO MANY LONELY, UN-MARRIED LADIES. AND IT'S REALLY TIME YOU SETTLED DOWN!"

"OOM FOOYAT FELL BEFORE WINNIE THE WITCH, SIR CADOR HAS SURRENDERED TO GWYNN, HELOISE HAS CAPTURED OSK. WHO KNOWS, YOU MAY BE NEXT!"

SO VAL MOUNTS AND RIDES FOR CAMELOT AND HE TRAVELS SWIFTLY AS ONE DOES WHO TRAVELS ALONE

HAL FOSTER

"WELL, SEE WHO'S HERE!" EXCLAIMS VAL, SETTING THE TABLE FOR TWO. "IF IT ISN'T THE KNIGHT WHO WILL FACE ANY PERIL SAVE ONLY THE PROSPECT OF MATRIMONY!"

NEXT WEEK – **The Ambitious Boy**
643   6 – 5 – 49

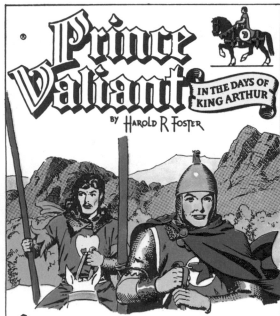

Prince Valiant

IN THE DAYS OF KING ARTHUR

BY HAROLD R. FOSTER

Synopsis: PRINCE VALIANT RIDES SWIFTLY TOWARD CAMELOT WHERE BRIGHT-EYED ALETA AND HIS MAN-CHILD AWAIT HIM. THIS ANNOYS SIR GAWAIN, FOR HE IS STILL FRIGHTENED; OF ALL THE GALLANT CREW WHO WENT TO THE CASTLE IILLWYNDE, ONLY HE HAS ESCAPED MATRIMONY!

IT IS THE CUSTOM OF YOUNG KNIGHTS SEEKING RE-NOWN TO HOLD SOME BRIDGE OR FORD AGAINST ALL COMERS. SO VAL AND GAWAIN ARE NOT SUR-PRISED WHEN THEY ARE CHALLENGED AT A FORD.

"HALT!" CALLS A CLEAR YOUNG VOICE, "I HOLD THIS FORD. WHO CROSSES MUST JOUST WITH ME!"

THEY TOSS A COIN AND GAWAIN WINS. "BE NOT TOO ROUGH," WHISPERS VAL, "FOR JUDGING BY HIS APPEARANCE, HE IS ONLY SOME UNTRIED YOUTH SEEKING EXPERIENCE."

THE YOUTH CHARGES INTO THE FRAY WITH MORE IMPETUOUS COURAGE THAN SKILL, AND THE VETER-AN KNIGHT PLUCKS HIM NEATLY FROM THE SADDLE!

VAL REMOVES THE BATTERED HELM, THE FRAYED MAIL HOOD, AND DISCOVERS A LAD NOT MORE THAN 14 YEARS OLD!

AT LAST HE IS ABLE TO SCRAMBLE TO HIS FEET: "I AM LEARNING TO BE A GREAT WARRIOR SO I CAN GO TO KING ARTHUR'S COURT AND BECOME A KNIGHT." THEN HE ADDS MISERABLY, "BUT FIVE TIMES HAVE I JOUSTED AND FIVE TIMES MET DEFEAT!"

"YOUNG IDIOT" SAYS GAWAIN, ROUGHLY, "YOU WILL BE MAIMED OR KILLED BEFORE YOU ARE OLD ENOUGH FOR PINFEATHERS! WE WILL TAKE YOU TO CAMELOT WITH US FOR TRAINING."

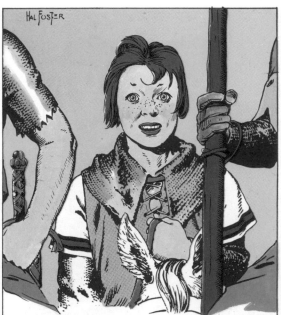

YOUNG GEOFFREY MOUNTS IN SILENCE WITHOUT SO MUCH AS A 'THANK YOU.' AND WHY? HE HAS MET THE FAMOUS PRINCE VALIANT; HE HAS EVEN JOUSTED WITH SIR GAWAIN AND HE IS GOING TO CAMELOT! THERE IS SUCH A LUMP IN HIS THROAT THAT HE CAN-NOT SPEAK!

644   6-12-49

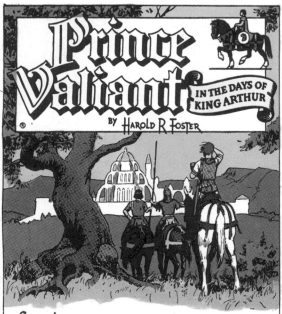

Prince Valiant
IN THE DAYS OF KING ARTHUR
BY HAROLD R FOSTER

Synopsis: THEY TOP THE LAST HILL AND CAMELOT LIES BEFORE THEM, ALL GLEAMING IN THE SUNLIGHT. THEIR QUEST IS OVER, THE WORK DONE. INTO THE SPACIOUS COURTYARD RIDE PRINCE VALIANT, SIR GAWAIN AND YOUNG GEOFFREY, AMID THE SHOUTED GREETINGS OF THEIR FRIENDS.

AND JEFF IS TURNED OVER TO SIR BALDWIN. "HERE, SIR, IS A PROMISING RECRUIT SIR GAWAIN AND I PICKED UP. SEE WHAT YOU CAN MAKE OF HIM."

THEN COMES THAT BREATHLESS MOMENT WHEN TIME STANDS STILL..... AND THE WEEKS OF LONELINESS ONLY MAKE THAT MOMENT SWEETER.

WHEN VAL LEFT ON HIS LAST QUEST, PRINCE ARN HAD BEEN A PINK AND LOVABLE NUISANCE, INDEFINITE AND HELPLESS. AS IF BY MAGIC, HIS SON HAS BECOME A PERSONALITY.

DEFINITE ARE THE FINE DARK EYES AND BROWS OF HIS SIRE; THE STRAIGHT SMALL NOSE OF HIS MOTHER AND... AS SO OFTEN HAPPENS WITH OFFSPRING OF BLONDE AND BRUNETTE... HE HAS A THATCH OF FLAMING RED HAIR.

FURTHER INVESTIGATION IS INTERRUPTED BY THE ENTRANCE OF GEOFFREY, BRINGING VAL'S SADDLE BAGS.

"THE TREES ARE FULL OF NUTS AT THIS SEASON," VAL EXPLAINS. *"THIS IS GEOFFREY. FOUND HIM IN THE WOODS; GOING TO MAKE A KNIGHT OF HIM."*

"AND A COURTEOUS, BRAVE KNIGHT HE WILL BE. NOW TAKE OFF THAT TUNIC AND I'LL HAVE KATWIN MEND IT FOR YOU." ALETA FEELS VERY MOTHERLY   AFTER ALL, SHE IS ALMOST TWENTY !

JEFF STAGGERS OUT INTO THE CORRIDOR . . . BLASTED BY A STRANGE, SWEET EMOTION . . . . . . PUPPY LOVE !

NEXT WEEK — **Dreams**.

HAL FOSTER

645   6-19-49

Prince Valiant
IN THE DAYS OF KING ARTHUR
BY HAROLD R FOSTER

Synopsis : 'GEOFFREY OF THE FORD' HE CALLS HIM-SELF AND BOASTS THAT HE HAS JOUSTED WITH THE GREAT SIR GAWAIN, IS FRIEND TO PRINCE VALIANT, THAT ALETA IS HIS 'LADY IN DOMNEI,' AND HE IS TO BECOME, IN THE VERY NEAR FUTURE, KNIGHT OF THE ROUND TABLE !
①

FOR THIS HE TAKES MANY A BEATING FROM THE OTHER SQUIRE RECRUITS, BUT FINALLY TEACHES THEM NOT TO LAUGH AT HIM.
②

A FEW DAYS LATER JEFF BURSTS INTO VAL'S CHAMBERS. "*I CAME TO CAMELOT TO BECOME A KNIGHT, NOT A WAITER AT TABLE ! TO LEARN TO USE A LANCE, NOT TURN A SPIT ! TO BE A WAR-RIOR, NOT A PAGE BOY !* "
③

"*NOW, HOW CAN YOU EVER BE A PAGE BOY WITH DIRTY HANDS AND SUCH UNTIDY HAIR ?* " CHIDES ALETA. "*YOU MUST PRACTICE HUMILITY IN THE KITCHENS, LEARN GOOD MANNERS WAITING AT TABLE AND COURTESY WHEN YOU BECOME A PAGE.* "
④

⑥

NEVER WOULD HE BETRAY HER CONFIDENCE IN HIM. HE WOULD BECOME SO CHIVALROUS A WARRIOR THAT KING ARTHUR HIMSELF WOULD BESTOW KNIGHTHOOD !

WEARING HER SLEEVE AS HIS GAGE HE WOULD BE TERRIBLE AND VICTOR-IOUS IN BATTLE.

PERHAPS HE MIGHT RISK HIS LIFE TO SAVE SIR VALIANT AND WIN HER GRATITUDE.

AS HER CHOSEN KNIGHT, AND WEARING HER FAVOR, HE WOULD, NATURALLY, WIN A GREAT TOURNAMENT.

AND MISTRESS ALETA, AS QUEEN OF BEAUTY, NATURALLY, WOULD PLACE THE CHAMPION'S CHAPLET UPON HIS BROW.

AND HE WOULD NEVER MARRY, HIS PURE HEART DEDICATED TO THE SERVICE OF HIS LADY.

BEYOND A DOUBT HE WOULD CONQUER SOME FABULOUS KINGDOM, AND AS A COURTLY GESTURE, GIVE HIS DEAR MISTRESS THE THRONE.

"*WOULD YOU EARN KNIGHTHOOD CHEAPLY ? IF SO, TAKE SERVICE WITH SOME MINOR KING. HERE AT KING ARTHUR'S COURT THE ROAD IS MUCH HARDER. BUT YOU WILL STAY; FOR YOU ARE TOO FINE A BOY TO ASPIRE TO AUGHT BUT THE BEST !* "
⑤

TO THE END WOULD HE SERVE HER ! AND WHEN HE HAD FOUGHT HIS LAST FIGHT AND WAS DYING GLORIOUSLY, SHE WOULD SHED A TEAR ON HIS FAITHFUL BREAST !

NEXT WEEK — *The Dangers of Peace.*

HAL FOSTER

Prince Valiant
IN THE DAYS OF KING ARTHUR
BY Harold R Foster

Synopsis: YOUNG GEOFFREY BEGINS HIS LONG CLIMB TOWARD KNIGHTHOOD. IN THE KITCHENS HE LEARNS HUMILITY. CARRYING WOOD AND WATER, TURNING THE SPIT, HE WORKS DILIGENTLY AND SOON BECOMES A PAGE.

FIRST HE MUST LEARN TO SERVE THE SQUIRES. HE LEARNS QUICKLY AND FINALLY IS APPOINTED TO THE TABLE OF THE LESSER NOBLES. HERE HE MUST LEARN COURTLY MANNERS AND THE COMPLICATED SYSTEM OF PRECEDENCE.

A BURNING AMBITION CARRIES HIM ON, FOR HE HAS GIVEN HIS BOYISH HEART TO ALETA. SHE IS TO BE HIS LADY; HE, HER KNIGHT-CHAMPION, AND DO MIGHTY DEEDS IN HER HONOR!

BUT THE ROAD IS HARD! IN THE EXERCISE YARD HE SOON LEARNS HOW FAR HE MUST GO TO BECOME EVEN A SQUIRE AND HIS LADY MUST BE SERVED ONLY BY THE BEST. A CHAMPION!

KING ARTHUR, TOO, HAS HIS PROBLEM. BRITAIN IS AT PEACE! NO VIKING RAIDS, NO SAXON INVASIONS; HUNDREDS OF TURBULENT WARRIORS IN CAMELOT WITH NOTHING TO DO!

FOR THE OLDER NOBLES HAVE GONE TO THEIR FIEFS TO GATHER THE RIPENING HARVEST AND PREPARE FOR THE COMING WINTER.

EVEN THE TOURNAMENTS CANNOT USE UP ALL THEIR ARDOR AND TOO MANY HEARTY YOUNG KNIGHTS ARE BEING KILLED!

THE KING INVENTS MANY MISSIONS TO KEEP THEM BUSY. AT LAST HE THINKS UP A GOOD ONE. HE CALLS ON PRINCE VALIANT WHO, DESPITE HIS MARRIAGE, HAS NOT YET SETTLED DOWN, AND SAYS:— "RIDE NORTH TO

'THE WALL.' SEE THAT IT IS BEING KEPT IN REPAIR AND DRIVE BACK ANY PICTS WHO HAVE SETTLED TOO CLOSE. I WILL CHOOSE YOUR COMPANIONS."

NEXT WEEK—The Deserter.
647   7-3-49

Prince Valiant

IN THE DAYS OF KING ARTHUR

BY HAROLD R FOSTER

Synopsis: PRINCE VALIANT AND HIS LAUGHING TROOP RIDE NORTHWARD TO 'THE WALL'. AND WELL THEY KNOW THAT THIS MISSION IS BUT AN EXCUSE TO KEEP THEM OUT OF MISCHIEF WHILE PEACE IS TROUBLING CAMELOT. SO ALETA RIDES WITH THEM FOR A WHILE.

GEOFFREY SEES THEM LEAVE. WHERE ARE THEY GOING? WILL THEY RETURN? NATURALLY HE SACRIFICES ALL CHANCES TO BECOME A KNIGHT OF THE ROUND TABLE TO FOLLOW HIS LADY.

ALETA BIDS FAREWELL TO HER HUSBAND AND RIDES HOMEWARD. SHE IS AN ISLAND GIRL, BORN TO THE SEA; NEVER CAN SHE RESIST THE INVITATION OF CLEAR, COOL WATER.

GEOFFREY DOES NOT KNOW THIS. AS HE GALLOPS BY, HE SEES HIS LADY FARTHER FROM SHORE THAN HE HAS EVER SEEN ANYONE IN HIS LIFE.

"BE CALM, MY (SPUTTER) LADY! I'LL (GURGLE) SAVE YOU." AND THE YOUNGSTER FLOUNDERS FORWARD, BARELY ABLE TO KEEP HIMSELF AFLOAT!

THOUGH SURELY DROWNING, HE IS STILL STRUGGLING TOWARD HER WHEN SHE REACHES HIM AND BRINGS HIM ASHORE.

HE WEEPS WITH SHAME; THAT HE, HER KNIGHT-TO-BE, SHOULD HAVE TO BE DRAGGED, LIKE A WET ROOSTER, FROM THE WATER! "FUNNY BOY," SHE LAUGHS, "DID THEY NOT TELL YOU NO KNIGHT IN ALL CAMELOT CAN BEST ME AT SWIMMING?"

"BUT I HONOR A BRAVE DEED. NOW RIDE ON TO SIR VALIANT AND STAY EVER AT HIS SIDE TO AID HIM IN TIME OF DANGER!"

NEXT WEEK – **A Friend at Court.**

648 7-10-49

Prince Valiant
IN THE DAYS OF KING ARTHUR
BY HAROLD R FOSTER

Synopsis : GEOFFREY SCRAMBLES INTO HIS ARMOR AND LEAPS FOR HIS MOUNT, EAGER TO BE OFF ON THE FIRST SERVICE TO HIS LADY. THEN HE STOPS; SOMETHING IS WRONG ! THE LADY ALETA IS STANDING BY HER HORSE.....LOOKING HELPLESS.

AS HE HOLDS THE STIRRUP AND HELPS HER MOUNT, HE KNOWS FULL WELL SHE CAN SPRING INTO THE SADDLE AS EASILY AS SHE RESCUED HIM FROM DROWNING IN THE LAKE ! BUT THEN, A LOVELY LADY EXPECTS GALLANTRY FROM A BRAVE GENTLEMAN.

THEN HE IS SPEEDING ON HIS MISSION."STAY CLOSE TO SIR VALIANT TO AID HIM WHEN PERIL IS NEAR," SHE HAD COMMANDED. HE HOPES THERE WILL BE PLENTY OF PERIL !

VAL'S TROOP IS PREPARING TO CAMP WHEN JEFF ARRIVES AND HIS FACE GOES WHITE WITH ANGER WHEN A ROAR OF LAUGHTER GREETS HIS MISSION.

"IT IS INDEED LAUGHABLE THAT AN AWKWARD BOY BE SENT TO PROTECT ME... FOR I AM THE MOST NIMBLE FIGHTER HEREABOUT !" AND VAL LOOKS AROUND, SMILING, TO SEE IF THERE IS ANYONE WHO WOULD CARE TO DISPUTE THAT POINT.

"BUT I WAS JUST ABOUT YOUR AGE WHEN I SAVED THE GREAT SIR GAWAIN FROM PERIL OF DEATH..... SO I DO NOT LAUGH. WELCOME, LAD !"

WHEN ALETA REACHES CAMELOT SHE GOES STRAIGHTWAY TO SIR BALDWIN TO EXPLAIN THE ABSENCE OF GEOFFREY AND ASK PARDON FOR HIS DESERTION. BUT THE RULES ARE STRICT AND JEFF'S NAME HAS ALREADY BEEN STRUCK FROM THE SCROLLS.

HE LISTENS IN GRIM SILENCE TO ALETA'S PLEA. "I ONLY HOPE MY BABY GROWS UP AS FINE AND BRAVE AS THAT GALLANT LAD !" SHE CONCLUDES.

SIR BALDWIN WATCHES HER WALK PROUDLY FROM THE ROOM, BUT HE DOES NOT RESTORE JEFF'S NAME TO THE LIST OF PAGE BOYS. INSTEAD HE ADDS IT TO THE ROSTER OF SQUIRES !

NEXT WEEK- **Val Refuses to Face the Foe !**
649   7-17-49

Synopsis: GEOFFREY STAYS SO CLOSE TO PRINCE VALIANT THAT HE IS EVER IN THE WAY, FOR HIS BELOVED MISTRESS HAS COMMANDED: *"STAY CLOSE TO SIR VALIANT TO AID HIM IN TIME OF PERIL."* AND THAT, COME FIRE OR HIGH WATER, HE WILL DO!

FOR THREE DAYS THEY FOLLOW NARROW TRAILS THROUGH THE DIM OAK FORESTS. THEN THEY COME TO THE OLD ROMAN ROAD LEADING NORTHWARD, AND TRAVEL IS EASY AND SWIFT.

VAL GETS HIS ROLLICKING TROOP PAST THE CITY OF YORK WITHOUT TOO MUCH DIFFICULTY AND THEY APPROACH THE TROUBLED LAND NEAR "THE WALL".

AND, THOUGH HE MAY SING AS LOUD AND JOKE AS MERRILY AS HIS MEN, VAL NEVER FORGETS HIS MISSION AND HIS SCOUTS ARE OUT EVEN THOUGH NO DANGER IS EXPECTED.

BUT THE UNEXPECTED HAPPENS! ONE SCOUT DUCKS JUST IN TIME AND RACES BACK TO HIS CAPTAIN WITH NEWS!

EVERYONE HAS BEEN AMUSED AT YOUNG GEOFFREY'S BOYISH DESIRE FOR ADVENTURE — EVEN VAL WOULD THINK HIS REPORT AN EXAGGERATION BUT FOR ONE THING, ... *"AND THEIR FACES WERE PAINTED BLUE,"* GEOFFREY SAYS.

ONLY THE PICTS PAINT THEMSELVES BLUE.... BUT PICTS A DAY'S MARCH FROM "THE WALL" CAN ONLY MEAN THAT THEY HAVE BROKEN THROUGH!

THEY RIDE TO THE CREST OF THE NEXT HILL WHERE VAL HALTS HIS TROOP LONG ENOUGH TO MAKE SURE THEY ARE SEEN BY THE PICTS; THEN HE ORDERS, *"RETREAT!"*

HIS MEN DO NOT OBEY; THEY ARE HEARTY FIGHTING MEN, SPOILING FOR A FIGHT. *"IS THE NOBLE PRINCE VALIANT AFRAID TO FACE A FEW SHORT-LEGGED PICTS?"* A VOICE MOCKS.

NEXT WEEK – **Serious Business.**

650   7-24-49

Prince Valiant
IN THE DAYS OF KING ARTHUR
BY HAROLD R FOSTER

Synopsis: WHEN PEACEFUL DAYS COME TO TROUBLE CAMELOT, KING ARTHUR SENDS THE MOST TROUBLESOME KNIGHTS ON A MISSION UNDER PRINCE VALIANT. WHEN, IN THE FACE OF THE ENEMY, HE ORDERS RETREAT, THEY SCOFF AT HIM.

AND VAL SCOFFS RIGHT BACK: *"GENTLEMEN, YOU ARE NOT AT A TOURNAMENT WHERE HEROIC DEEDS ARE DONE BEFORE THE ADMIRING EYES OF FAIR LADIES!"*

THEN HIS MANNER CHANGES. *"THIS IS BUSINESS,"* HE SNAPS. *"RETREAT!"*

ONCE OUT OF SIGHT OF THE ENEMY VAL BARKS HIS ORDERS, *"RIDE TO YONDER HILL AND PREPARE TO DEFEND IT.... DO NOT UN-SADDLE, BE READY TO RIDE AT MY SIGNAL!"*

THEN TAKING YOUNG GEOFFREY WITH HIM, VAL FINDS A POINT FROM WHICH TO WATCH AND WAIT.

THE PICTS ARE WILY FIGHTING MEN. THEY PAINT THEMSELVES BLUE AND GREEN SO THEY CAN CROUCH, UNSEEN, AMONG THE HEATHER. BUT VAL'S RETREAT DRAWS THEM FROM THEIR AMBUSH TO FOLLOW, AND THEY COME SWARMING ACROSS THE HILL.
AND NOW THEIR NUMBER CAN BE SEEN. THIS IS NO MERE RAID, BUT A FULL SCALE INVASION THROUGH SOME BREECH IN "THE WALL!"

NEXT WEEK — **Into Scotland.**

Prince Valiant
IN THE DAYS OF KING ARTHUR
BY HAROLD R FOSTER

Synopsis : PRINCE VALIANT HAS BEEN SENT TO INSPECT "THE WALL" BUILT LONG AGO BY THE ROMANS TO KEEP BACK THE WILD PICTS OF SCOTLAND. BUT HIS TROOP MEETS AN ARMY OF THE BLUE-PAINTED FIGHTERS BEFORE EVER REACHING "THE WALL".

HE SENDS JEFF BACK TO THE TROOP. "*TELL THEM TO CIRCLE WIDE AROUND THE PICTS, RIDE NORTH AND MEET ME AT "THE WALL".*"

THEN HE TOO MOUNTS AND RIDES SWIFTLY NORTHWARD.

EMPEROR HADRIAN HAD CAUSED THIS WALL TO BE BUILT LONG AGO WHEN ROME RULED THE KNOWN WORLD, AND KING ARTHUR KEEPS A GARRISON HERE. IT STRETCHES AWAY OVER THE HILLS AND ALL IS QUIET— TOO QUIET. VAL DISMOUNTS AND APPROACHES CAUTIOUSLY.

AT THE FIRST MILECASTLE HE LEARNS THE REASON FOR THIS QUIET. THE PICTS HAVE SURPRISED THE GARRISON.

ASCENDING TO THE TOP OF "THE WALL," VAL SCANS THE COUNTRYSIDE. FAR TO THE WEST HE CAN DISCERN DISTANT FIGURES MOVING TOWARD THE NEXT MILECASTLE... THERE THE BREAK-THROUGH MUST BE !

DARKNESS IS FALLING WHEN HIS TROOP ARRIVES. VAL HAS DONE SOME SCOUTING AND HAS HIS PLANS ALL LAID.

THEN THE SMALL GATEWAY LEADING INTO SCOTLAND IS OPENED AND THEY RIDE FORTH INTO THE WINDY DARKNESS ON THE ENEMY SIDE OF "THE WALL."

NEXT WEEK—**Val Lets the Enemy Through.**

Prince Valiant
IN THE DAYS OF KING ARTHUR
BY Harold R Foster

Synopsis : THROUGH "THE WALL" AND INTO THE LAND OF THE PICTS PRINCE VALIANT LEADS HIS TROOP. KING ARTHUR HAD PLANNED THIS MISSION ONLY TO GET THE MORE TROUBLESOME KNIGHTS AWAY FROM CAMELOT, BUT NOW THEY ARE FACED WITH AN INVASION OF BRITAIN BY THE PICTS.

THEY APPROACH THE CAPTURED MILECASTLE FROM THE NORTH. THE GATE IS AJAR, FOR THE PICTS EXPECTED NO DANGER FROM THEIR OWN COUNTRY.

VAL AND HIS MEN ENTER AND CLOSE THE GATE BEHIND THEM. IN THE SMOKY GLARE OF THE TORCHES THE GRIM WORK BEGINS.

AFTER SUFFERING THE BOREDOM OF MONTHS OF PEACE THE YOUNG KNIGHTS RETURN TO WORK WITH GUSTO !

VAL IS QUITE PLEASED. THEY HAVE RECAPTURED THE GATEWAY THROUGH WHICH THE FIERCE PICTS ARE INVADING BRITAIN, AND THEY HAVE TAKEN A GREAT STORE OF SUPPLIES.

NEXT MORNING THE FUN BEGINS. THE INDEPENDENT LITTLE PICTS COME STREAMING DOWN FROM THEIR HILLS, CARRYING THEIR WEAPONS AND SUPPLIES, THEIR FACES BLUE WITH WARPAINT.

653 8-14-49

THEY ENTER THE GATE. THEY LOSE AN ARGUMENT. THEY GO THROUGH INTO BRITAIN...

BUT UNARMED, WITHOUT FOOD, AND IN A LAND LAID WASTE BY THEIR OWN ADVANCING COMRADES !

NEXT WEEK - **Starvation and Panic.**

Prince Valiant
IN THE DAYS OF KING ARTHUR
BY HAROLD R FOSTER

Synopsis: DOWN FROM THEIR MISTY HILLS COME THE PICTS TO CROWD THROUGH THE OPENING IN THE GREAT WALL INTO BRITAIN. BUT WITHIN THE MILECASTLE ARE PRINCE VALIANT AND HIS KNIGHTS, AND EACH PICT IS DISARMED AS HE PASSES THROUGH!

THE PICTS WHO HAD BREACHED THE WALL EARLIER SWEEP SOUTHWARD UNCHECKED, LAYING WASTE THE LAND. BUT THE COUNTRYSIDE DOES NOT PROVIDE ENOUGH FOOD FOR SUCH AN ARMY AND NO SUPPLIES COME UP FROM THE REAR!

INSTEAD GREAT NUMBERS OF THEIR COMRADES ARRIVE UNARMED AND STARVING TO TELL OF PRINCE VALIANT CALMLY STANDING OVER BOTH THEIR SUPPLIES AND THEIR MEANS OF RETREAT!

AHEAD LIES THE CITY OF YORK, A RICH PRIZE, THEIRS FOR THE TAKING. NOT ONCE HAVE THEY THOUGHT OF RETURNING UNTIL THEY LEARN THE WAY IS BLOCKED. THEN ALL EYES TURN TOWARD THEIR NORTHERN HILLS!

"GENTLEMEN," SMILES VAL, MOUNTING HIS STEED, "YOU WANTED SOME FIGHTING. IN A FEW DAYS THERE SHOULD BE PLENTY!" AND HE RIDES AWAY ALONG THE WALL.

HE WISELY CHOOSES TO RIDE ON THE ENEMY SIDE OF "THE WALL", KNOWING THAT EVERY PICT HEREABOUT HAS JOINED THE INVASION.

AT A POINT SOME DISTANCE FROM THE BREAK-THROUGH THE SENTINELS ON THE WALL ARE SURPRISED TO SEE ONE OF KING ARTHUR'S KNIGHTS RIDE UP FROM THE NORTH AND DEMAND ADMITTANCE!

TO THE CAPTAIN OF THE GUARDS VAL SAYS: "SEND SWIFT MESSENGERS ALONG THE WALL TO TELL EVERY MOUNTED MAN TO MEET HERE!"

WITHIN A FEW DAYS VAL IS LEADING THE POOREST-LOOKING TROOP HE HAS EVER SEEN AGAINST THE INVADING HORDES OF FIERCE HILLMEN!

NEXT WEEK - **The Raiders.**

Synopsis: THE INVADING HORDE OF PICTS HESITATES BEFORE THEM IS THE CITY OF YORK, A RICH PRIZE, THEIRS FOR THE TAKING BEHIND THEM THERE IS SOMETHING ELSE AGAIN!

PRINCE VALIANT LEADS HIS MOUNTED TROOPS BACK AND FORTH BEHIND THE ENEMY LINES LIKE A DEADLY SCYTHE SWIFTLY THEY STRIKE AND ARE GONE AGAIN.

WEARY, EXHAUSTED--BUT THEY HAVE CUT OFF COMPLETELY ALL COMMUNICATION BETWEEN THE INVADERS AND THEIR ROCKY HOMELAND.

THEY, TOO, ARE CUT OFF AND WILL BE WIPED OUT SHOULD THE PICTS TURN HOMEWARD; FOR THEY NUMBER TWO HUNDRED AGAINST THOUSANDS YET IT IS THEIR DUTY TO TURN THE PICTS HOMEWARD

THEN VAL CHANGES HIS TACTICS. THROUGH "THE WALL" INTO SCOTLAND THEY GO IN A GREAT SWEEPING RAID, BURNING VILLAGES AND CAPTURING THE WOMEN AND CHILDREN.

THESE, FRIGHTENED BUT UNHARMED, ARE SET FREE IN BRITAIN TO JOIN THEIR MEN AT THE FIGHTING FRONT.... AND TELL OF THE RAIDS ON THEIR VILLAGES!

THE INVASION WAVERS AND COMES TO A HALT, CONFUSED, UNDECIDED AHEAD THERE IS PLUNDER; BEHIND, THEIR HOMES ARE BURNING!

THE RETREAT BEGINS VAL RETIRES TO THE MILECASTLE AND SETS ALL IN ORDER FOR THE FINAL STRUGGLE

NEXT WEEK - **The Hopeless Struggle**

Prince Valiant

IN THE DAYS OF KING ARTHUR

BY HAROLD R FOSTER

Synopsis: FRIENDS AND ENEMIES ARRIVE AT THE SAME TIME! SIR JULIAN, GUARDSMAN OF "THE WALL," HAS FOUGHT HIS WAY, STEP BY STEP, BACK ALONG THAT PART OF "THE WALL" THE PICTS HAD TAKEN IN THEIR FIRST ONSLAUGHT. AND THE FIRST OF THE RETREATING INVADERS ARE GATHERING BEFORE THE MILECASTLE!

"OUR LITTLE BLUE-EYED PLAYMATES MUST BE ALLOWED TO SCALE THE WALLS TO THEIR OWN LAND, BUT EVERY GATE THROUGH WHICH THEY CAN RETURN MUST BE HELD AT ALL COSTS!"

BUT HOW? COUNTLESS THOUSANDS CAN BE SEEN APPROACHING, EACH ONE A HARDY FIGHTING MAN.

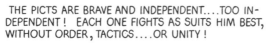

THE PICTS ARE BRAVE AND INDEPENDENT....TOO INDEPENDENT! EACH ONE FIGHTS AS SUITS HIM BEST, WITHOUT ORDER, TACTICS....OR UNITY!

VAL PLACES HIS MAIL-CLAD WARRIORS SO THERE ARE THREE TO OPPOSE EACH ATTACKER.

GRIM AND EFFICIENT BUTCHERY! AND STILL THEY COME ON.... NEARLY SMOTHERING THE DEFENDERS BY SHEER WEIGHT. THEN VAL GIVES AN ORDER STRANGE TO THE EARS OF DESPERATE FIGHTING MEN!

"DO NOT KILL! STRIKE TO WOUND!" BUT THE SCHEME IS EFFECTIVE AS THE WOUNDED, STRUGGLING BACK FROM THE PRESS, INTERFERE WITH THEIR COMRADES.

THE DAY HAS BEEN WON — BUT WHAT OF THE NEXT.... AND THE NEXT? THEIR SITUATION IS UTTERLY HOPELESS! SO HOPELESS INDEED THAT VAL RISES, YAWNS AND STRETCHES. HE ALSO GRINS....THERE IS NOTHING MORE TO WORRY ABOUT NOW!

NEXT WEEK- **The Bribe.**

656--9-4

656

BEFORE DAYLIGHT LADDERS ARE DROPPED ALONG THE WALL AND ROPES PLACED IN CONVENIENT PLACES FOR THE PICTS TO FIND

A MOUNTED TROOP IS SENT THROUGH INTO SCOTLAND AND THE DOORWAY SEALED UP BEHIND THEM.... IF THE MILECASTLE FALLS TO THE PICTS, THEY WILL NOT HAVE AN ENTRANCE BY WHICH TO RETURN

AT DAYBREAK THE BATTLE FOR THE MILECASTLE IS RESUMED   BUT THE LADDERS HAVE BEEN FOUND AND THE FIRST PICTS TO MOUNT THE WALL SEE ......

.... SMOKE FROM THEIR BURNING VILLAGES. THE MOUNTED TROOP IS DOING ITS WORK WELL !

SOME CAPTIVES ARE TAKEN, AND VAL LIES CHEERFULLY: *"OH, LET THEM GO. KING ARTHUR WILL ARRIVE WITH HIS ARMY SOON AND THEY WILL WANT SOME SPORT ! "*

THEN VAL LOOKS AT GEOFFREY, SO YOUNG AND EAGER... TOO YOUNG TO DIE ! SO HE SAYS: *"YOU MUST CARRY A MESSAGE TO THE KING. IT IS IMPORTANT. DO NOT FAIL ! "* AND SENDS HIM AWAY.

A PRISONER IS TAKEN, THEN GIVEN A MESSAGE TO DELIVER TO TWO CLAN LEADERS, ODER AND 'THE HAMMER'. A SHORT TRUCE IS ARRANGED.

PRINCE VALIANT, KNIGHT OF THE ROUND TABLE AND RENOWNED FOR DEEDS OF BRAVERY, OFFERS TO BRIBE HIS FOES !

NEXT WEEK— **Bad Tempers.**

Prince Valiant
IN THE DAYS OF KING ARTHUR
BY HAROLD R FOSTER

Synopsis: STANDING IN THE PATH OF THE RETURNING PICTS, PRINCE VALIANT AND HIS MEN FACE ALMOST CERTAIN DESTRUCTION WITH CHEERFUL IMPUDENCE VAL OFFERS TO BRIBE WITH GOLD TWO RIVAL CHIEFTAINS!

"TO YOU, ODER, WILL I GIVE THIS PURSE OF GOLD IF YOU WILL TAKE YOUR MEN AWAY. AND HERE IS A HANDFUL OF COINS FOR 'THE HAMMER' IF HE WILL DO THE SAME."

ALTHOUGH THE BRIBE IS TRIVIAL THE INSULT IS NOT! 'THE HAMMER'S' FACE IS DARK WITH ANGER: "WHY OFFER ME LESS THAN ODER?"

"BECAUSE HE IS THE GREATER WARRIOR," AN-SWERS VAL INNOCENTLY. "HAVE YOU NOT HEARD HIM BOAST OF HIS LEADERSHIP?"

"BOAST! BOAST!" THUNDERS 'THE HAMMER', "THAT IS ALL THAT MOUTHY WINDBAG CAN DO! WHY, WITH MY BARE HANDS....!"

"DEAR ME!" MUTTERS VAL PLEASANTLY, "SUCH BAD TEMPERS! I HOPE IT IS NOT BECAUSE OF ANYTHING I SAID!"

CLAN MEMBERS RUSH TO THE AID OF THEIR CHIEFTAINS. SOON THERE ARE MORE PICTS FIGHTING PICTS THAN ARE FIGHTING VAL'S MEN, AND THESE WEARY HEROES HAVE A MUCH NEEDED REST.

NO LONGER IS IT SAFE NORTH OF 'THE WALL,' FOR THE PICTS ARE COMING OVER WHEREVER THEY CAN AND DEATH COMES CLOSE TO YOUNG GEOFFREY.

658 9-18-49

BUT HE WINS TO A DISTANT MILECASTLE AND IS LET THROUGH INTO BRITAIN. AHEAD OF HIM IS THE LONG ROAD TO CAMELOT AND MANY DANGERS!

NEXT WEEK— **The Long Ride.**

Prince Valiant
IN THE DAYS OF KING ARTHUR
BY HAROLD R FOSTER

NOW, CAUGHT BY THE RETREATING HORDES THEY FIGHT WITH LIGHT-HEARTED ABANDON AS BECOMES MEN WHO ARE ABOUT TO DIE.

Synopsis: ONCE AGAIN THE PICTS SWARM DOWN FROM SCOTTISH HILLS TO PLUNDER BRITAIN. BUT PRINCE VALIANT AND HIS NIMBLE HORSEMEN GET IN BEHIND THE INVADERS AND WITH SWEEPING RAIDS BURN THEIR VILLAGES AND CUT OFF THEIR SUPPLIES.

THROUGH THE LAND LAID WASTE BY THE INVASION RIDES GEOFFREY, CARRYING A MESSAGE TO THE KING.

AND OFTEN HE IS IN DANGER FROM STRAGGLING PICTS. EACH TIME HE IS SAVED BY THE SPEED OF HIS MOUNT.

BIT BY BIT HE ABANDONS HIS PRECIOUS ARMOR, FOR HE MUST GET EVERY OUNCE OF SPEED FROM HIS HORSE.

HE IS, INDEED, MORE MINDFUL OF HIS MOUNT THAN OF HIMSELF; YET, EVEN RESTING OR GRAZING, HE MOVES EVER FORWARD.

KING ARTHUR RIDES TO A DISTANT MEADOW TO FLY A NEW HAWK AT THE GROUSE, BUT SOME HORSE THIEF SPOILS HIS DAY BY EXCHANGING A FOUNDERED NAG FOR HIS GREAT BLACK CHARGER.

AND GEOFFREY, SWOONING WITH WEARINESS, THUNDERS INTO CAMELOT WITH A MESSAGE FOR THE KING.

BUT WHERE IS THE KING? HOURS LATER AN ANGRY ROAR HERALDS HIS APPROACH AS, FOOTSORE AND TIRED, HE LEADS A SPENT HORSE THROUGH THE PORTALS.

NEXT WEEK— **The Message.**

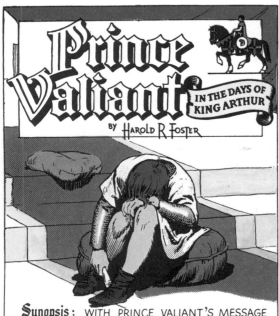

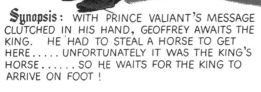

Synopsis: WITH PRINCE VALIANT'S MESSAGE CLUTCHED IN HIS HAND, GEOFFREY AWAITS THE KING. HE HAD TO STEAL A HORSE TO GET HERE..... UNFORTUNATELY IT WAS THE KING'S HORSE...... SO HE WAITS FOR THE KING TO ARRIVE ON FOOT !

THE KING LIMPS IN AND GLARES AT THE MISCREANT. THEN HE TAKES THE MESSAGE AND READS ALOUD THE SIMPLE, CHEERFUL LINES.

" SIRE .— THE PICTS BROKE THROUGH BUT WE HAVE INDUCED THEM TO RETURN. WE HAVE HAD SPLENDID WEATHER FOR FIGHTING. WOULD ADVISE IMMEDIATE STRENGTHENING OF 'THE WALL' HEREABOUTS."

" BUT, SIRE, HE DID NOT TELL ALL ! " CRIES GEOFFREY, " OF HOW HE LED US CRASHING THROUGH TO THE REAR OF THAT VAST ARMY, TO SWEEP BACK AND FORTH LIKE A DEADLY SCYTHE ! "

" NIGHT AND DAY HE LED US UNTIL WE COULD NO LONGER LIFT A SWORD FOR WEARINESS.... BUT WE CUT OFF THEIR SUPPLIES ! "

" THEN HE LED US ON A SWIFT RAID INTO THE LAND OF THE PICTS, AND THE INVADERS COULD LOOK BACK AND SEE THE SMOKE FROM THEIR BURNING VILLAGES ! "

" YES ! HE INDUCED THE PICTS TO TURN BACK-- TO TURN BACK UPON HIM ! BEHIND OUR FRAIL DEFENSES WE STOOD WHILE THE PICTS IN COUNT- LESS THOUSANDS SWARMED ANGRILY UPON US. PRINCE VALIANT WAS SINGING AS I LEFT."

THEN ALETA HELPS THE WEARY LAD TO HIS FEET AND LEADS HIM AWAY.

NEXT WEEK- **More Thievery**.

Prince Valiant
IN THE DAYS OF KING ARTHUR
BY HAROLD R FOSTER

Synopsis: GEOFFREY DELIVERS PRINCE VALIANT'S MESSAGE TO THE KING, AND THEN ALETA LEADS HIM AWAY.

AND GETS FROM HIM THE FULL STORY OF THE DESPERATE FIGHTING AT "THE WALL". *"SIR VALIANT WAS SINGING AS I LEFT,"* SAYS GEFF. ALETA SHUDDERS, FOR WELL SHE KNOWS THAT VAL IS HAPPIEST WHEN THE ODDS ARE ALL AGAINST HIM!

SHORTLY THEREAFTER SHE DRESSES FOR RIDING, AND HER TWO SERVITORS PACK HER SADDLE-BAGS IN SILENCE. FOR THIS IS ALETA THE MISTRESS, NOT THE SMALL GIRL THEY HAVE SO OFTEN PETTED AND FONDLY SCOLDED.

THEN SHE HOLDS HER BABY FOR A BREATHLESS MOMENT-- FOR THIS IS THEIR FIRST PARTING.

AND SHE MUST CARRY MANY MESSAGES FROM WIVES, SWEETHEARTS AND MOTHERS OF THE FIGHTING MEN. THESE LADIES ARE BRAVE AND GALLANT AS THEIR MEN, FOR THEY BEAR THE GNAWING ANXIETY OF WAITING, WAITING THROUGH ENDLESS DAYS, WITH CALM DIGNITY.

WHEN GEFF AWAKES FROM HIS LONG SLEEP HE LEARNS HIS BELOVED MISTRESS IS RIDING TOWARD THE PERILOUS NORTH.

HIS OWN MOUNT IS STILL UNFIT FOR TRAVEL. WELL, IF ONE MUST STEAL A HORSE, WHY NOT THE BEST?

661 10-9-49

OUT INTO THE NIGHT RIDES GEOFFREY ON ONE OF THE KING'S OWN HUNTERS! NEXT WEEK- **Aleta among the Picts.**

Synopsis : FAR TO THE NORTH PRINCE VALIANT IS IN MORTAL DANGER. SO ALETA RIDES SWIFTLY NORTHWARD. SHE IS USED TO THE WOUNDS AND BRUISES VAL RECEIVES IN THE COURSE OF BUSINESS, BUT THIS IS GOING TOO FAR; SHE INTENDS TO PUT A STOP TO THE NONSENSE! GEOFFREY JOINS THEM, AND IT IS QUITE APPARENT THAT HE HAS STOLEN ONE OF KING ARTHUR'S HORSES.

ALETA SETS THE PACE RIGHT UP TO THE LIMIT OF ENDURANCE FOR HORSES AND MEN. SOON THEY REACH THE WRECKAGE OF THE INVASION.

BUT LONG SINCE THE PICTS HAVE STORMED THE BARRICADE IN A SCREAMING TIDE, AND VAL HAS ORDERED HIS MEN TO RETREAT INTO THE MILECASTLE!

BUT HE HAS COVERED THEIR RETREAT UNTIL HE GOES DOWN!

AND NOW THE EXHAUSTED SURVIVORS ARE MAKING THEIR LAST STAND!

VAL REFUSES TO DIE; HOLDING HIS GAPING WOUND TOGETHER HE CHEERS ON HIS MEN.

THEN SUDDENLY THE HORRID DIN OF BATTLE DIES AWAY INTO AWED SILENCE! VAL HEARS A VOICE MUTTER: "IT'S ALETA!"

10-16-49

INTO THAT SWEATING, PANTING MOB OF SAVAGES WALKS ALETA, DAINTY, CALM, ALOOF!

NEXT WEEK - **And the Nonsense Stops.**

Prince Valiant
IN THE DAYS OF KING ARTHUR
BY Harold R Foster

Synopsis: WITH THE LAST OF HIS STRENGTH PRINCE VALIANT DRAGS HIMSELF TO THE PARAPET AND LOOKS DOWN IN HORROR AS ALETA WALKS CALMLY INTO THE RANKS OF HIS SAVAGE ENEMIES!

SHE IS SUPERB! THOUGH HER HEART IS SICK WITH ANXIETY SHE DOES NOT DARE EVEN GLANCE AT THE DEAD TO SEE IF VAL IS AMONG THEM. INSTEAD, EVERY INCH A QUEEN, SHE CALMLY ORDERS: *"BRING ME YOUR LEADER!"*

"DO YOU WISH FOOD FOR YOUR MEN?" SHE ASKS. WELL SHE KNOWS THE PICTS ARE STARVING, FOR GEOFFREY HAS TOLD HER THAT ALL THEIR PROVISIONS ARE IN THE MILECASTLE!

THEN, FOR THE FIRST TIME, SHE LOOKS UP TO THE DEFENDERS: *"THROW DOWN SOME PROVISIONS FOR THESE MEN!"*

FEED THEIR WEAKENING ENEMIES! THE KNIGHTS HESITATE. *"OBEY HER!"* WHISPERS VAL AS HE SINKS INTO UNCONSCIOUSNESS.

THE BUNDLES COME HURTLING DOWN AND THERE IS A MAD SCRAMBLE AS THE STARVING MEN FIGHT FOR THE FOOD.

NO ONE NOTICES, OR CARES, THAT A LADDER IS LOWERED AND ALETA MOUNTS TO THE MILE-CASTLE ROOF.

"THE REST OF YOUR FOOD WILL BE THROWN OVER ON THE OTHER SIDE OF THE WALL; GO OVER AND GET IT OR STAY HERE AND STARVE!"

NEXT WEEK— **Surgery**.

Synopsis: THE MILECASTLE AND ALL ITS GALLANT DEFENDERS ARE DOOMED BY THE HORDE OF STARVING PICTS SURGING AGAINST THEM. BUT ALETA ARRIVES, ORDERS THE DEFENDERS TO FEED THEIR ENEMIES, WHICH STOPS THE FIGHTING; THEN HAS THEM TOSS THEIR GREAT STORE OF PROVISIONS OVER 'THE WALL,' AND THE INVASION OF BRITAIN IS OVER.

AND ON A DISTANT HILL GEOFFREY FAINTS. HE HAD BEEN ORDERED TO STAY BACK WHILE HIS BELOVED MISTRESS WALKED, ALONE, AMONG THE SAVAGE PICTS. THE STRAIN HAS BEEN TOO MUCH!

AND NOW, ALETA, NO LONGER AN IMPERIOUS QUEEN, BUT A FRIGHTENED SMALL WIFE, TENDS HER HUSBAND.

PANIC GRIPS HER AS SHE SEES HIS YOUNG LIFE SLOWLY SLIPPING THROUGH THE GAPING AXE WOUND IN HIS SIDE.

BUT SHE WHISPERS A SMALL PRAYER, HER EYES GROW CALM AND HER CHIN COMES UP. SHE IS READY FOR HER GREAT BATTLE WITH GRAND-FATHER DEATH!

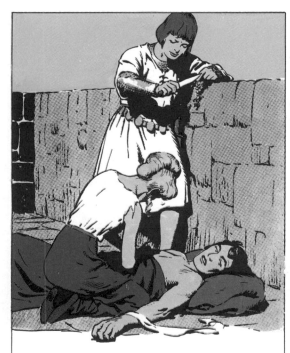

BANDAGES WILL NOT CLOSE THE WOUND, SO METAL RINGS FROM HIS CHAIN ARMOR ARE FASHIONED INTO CLIPS.

A TENDER, ROUND, WHITE ARM AND A COLD, CRUEL KNIFE ARE GIVEN TO GEFF WITH ORDERS WHICH HE MUST OBEY.

CRUEL TIMES CALL FOR CRUEL METHODS. SO, THROUGH A HOLLOW REED, TWO YOUNG HEARTS GIVE THEIR BLOOD THAT ANOTHER MIGHT LIVE.

NEXT WEEK— **The Long Fight.**

664

Prince Valiant
IN THE DAYS OF KING ARTHUR
BY HAROLD R FOSTER

Synopsis: THROUGH THE NIGHT PRINCE VALIANT MUTTERS WEAKLY IN HIS TROUBLED SLEEP. WITH THE DAWN COME THE CARRION CROWS AND THE RISING SUN MAKES WORSE THE STENCH FROM THE BATTLEFIELD. THE PESTILENCE THAT FOLLOWS WAR WILL SOON BE UPON THEM.

A LITTER IS CAREFULLY CONSTRUCTED.

TENDERLY THEIR LEADER IS LIFTED ONTO THE LITTER.

THEY TRAVEL SLOWLY EASTWARD ATOP THE WALL. THE GUARDS ALONG THE WALL ARE GRIM AND BITTER MEN, CRIMINALS MOSTLY, SENT TO THIS DESOLATE OUTPOST AS PUNISHMENT, BUT ONE AND ALL SALUTE THE DARING LEADER WHO, WITH BUT 200 MEN, TURNED BACK 10,000 PICTS. AND, BECAUSE THEY ADMIRE HIS BRAVERY, THEY WILL BE BETTER MEN HEREAFTER.

AT LAST, THEY NEAR THE SEA AND, IN THE LITTLE TOWN OF NEWCASTLE, FIND SHELTER.

ALETA'S FACE IS THIN AND PALE WITH WEARINESS; HER GRAY EYES ARE SHADOWED BY ANXIETY; SLEEPLESSNESS HAS LINED HER FACE.

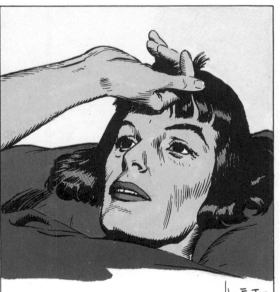

HAL FOSTER

BUT WHEN, AT LAST, VAL OPENS HIS EYES, IT IS STILL THE MOST BEAUTIFUL FACE IN THE WORLD.

NEXT WEEK — *The Shadow Passes.*

Prince Valiant

IN THE DAYS OF KING ARTHUR

BY HAROLD R FOSTER

Synopsis: PRINCE VALIANT AND ALL HIS GALLANT BAND ARE ABOUT TO DIE GLORIOUSLY AS BEFITS BRAVE KNIGHTS. THEN ALETA ARRIVES AND, WITH UNROMANTIC COMMON SENSE, PUTS A STOP TO THE WAR

FOR A LONG WHILE THE FLAME OF LIFE FLUTTERS LIKE A CANDLE IN A WINDY PLACE.

BUT VAL AND ALETA HAVE TOO MUCH TO LIVE FOR, AND DEATH IS DRIVEN BACK INTO THE SHADOWS.

ALETA GOES SHOPPING; FOR SHE HAS TORN HER GARMENTS TO MAKE BANDAGES.

THE MARKET PLACE IS CROWDED AND ALETA IS SURPRISED AT THE NUMBER OF NORTHMEN, VIKING TRADERS FROM DISTANT THULE.

THIS GIVES HER AN IDEA; IT WILL BE MANY WEEKS BEFORE VAL CAN UNDERTAKE THE LONG, PAINFUL RIDE BACK TO CAMELOT. BUT A SEA VOYAGE......!

ON A SEA VOYAGE HE COULD REST AND REGAIN HIS STRENGTH. HER MIND IS MADE UP; SHE WILL TAKE VAL HOME !

"GEOFFREY, RIDE SWIFTLY TO CAMELOT AND GIVE THIS PURSE TO KATWIN. TELL HER TO BRING PRINCE ARN HITHER. SHE WILL ARRANGE THE MEANS."

POOR GEOFF ! HE MUST DO HIS MISTRESS'S BIDDING. AND AT CAMELOT THEY ARE WAITING TO QUESTION HIM ABOUT THE THEFT OF KING ARTHUR'S HORSES !

HE IS WILLING TO GIVE HIS LIFE GLORIOUSLY FOR HIS DEAR MISTRESS BUT BEING HUNG AS A HORSE THIEF IS QUITE ANOTHER THING !

NEXT WEEK —Arrested.   HAL FOSTER

Prince Valiant
IN THE DAYS OF KING ARTHUR
BY HAROLD R FOSTER

Synopsis: NO KNIGHT EVER SERVED HIS LADY FAIR MORE FAITHFULLY THAN YOUNG GEOFFREY. HE HAD DESERTED HIS POST AS PAGE-BOY AND EVEN STOLEN KING ARTHUR'S HORSES TO RENDER SERVICE TO LADY ALETA.

NOW, AT HER BIDDING, HE IS RETURNING. IT IS A VERY UNHAPPY LAD WHO RIDES SOUTHWARD ACROSS THE WINDY HILLS.

THE FORESTS ARE AFLAME WITH AUTUMN COLORS, BUT GEOFF DOES NOT NOTICE THEIR SPLENDOR; HE IS TROUBLED WITH A GROWING FEAR.

CAMELOT ARISES, ALL GLEAMING IN THE DISTANCE, AND GEOFF HALTS. SHALL HE GO ON AND FACE HANGING AS A HORSE THIEF?

OR SHALL HE ENTER BY STEALTH AND DELIVER ALETA'S MESSAGE TO KATWIN?

THEN HE REMEMBERS HOW PRINCE VALIANT COVERED HIS MEN'S RETREAT, LAUGHING IN THE FACE OF HIS FOES UNTIL HE WENT DOWN..

AND HOW MISTRESS ALETA WALKED ALONE INTO THE RANKS OF THE SAVAGE PICTS.

667-11-20-49

HE, TOO, WILL BE BRAVE AND FEARLESS. SO HE RIDES BOLDLY INTO CAMELOT ON THE KING'S HORSE...

HAL FOSTER

AND IS ARRESTED, VERY UNROMANTICALLY, LIKE ANY OTHER HORSE THIEF.

NEXT WEEK— **The Message.**

Prince Valiant
IN THE DAYS OF KING ARTHUR
BY Harold R Foster

Synopsis: SO GEOFFREY RIDES INTO CAMELOT WITH ALETA'S MESSAGE AND IS PROMPTLY ARRESTED FOR TWICE STEALING KING ARTHUR'S HORSE AND FOR DESERTING HIS POST !

"SIR BALDWIN, GRANT ME TIME TO DELIVER MISTRESS ALETA'S MESSAGE BEFORE YOU HANG ME ! "

SIR BALDWIN SIGHS -- WHY IS IT THAT THE BRAVEST, MOST LOVABLE LADS ALWAYS SEEM TO BE THE MOST TROUBLESOME ? "YOU WILL BE GRANTED NO FAVORS UNTIL YOUR TRIAL TO-MORROW ! "

"BUT IT IS FOR THE LADY ALETA ! I MUST ! " CRIES GEOFF AS HE TEARS HIMSELF FREE .

THROUGH THE ECHOING CORRIDORS HE RACES, TRYING DESPERATELY TO COMPLETE HIS MISSION BEFORE MEETING HIS DOOM !

WHEN AT LAST HE FINDS KATWIN, TILLICUM AND THE YOUNG PRINCE ARN HE IS ALL OUT OF BREATH .

" THE LADY ALETA AND SIR VALIANT ARE GOING TO THULE. YOU ARE TO MEET THEM AT NEWCASTLE WITH PRINCE ARN ! "

"HERE IS MONEY FOR THE JOURNEY. YOU ARE TO FIND MEANS TO GET THERE. HURRY ! "

THEN, WITH ONE MORE COUNT AGAINST HIM, HE IS LED AWAY.

NEXT WEEK—Banished.

Prince Valiant

IN THE DAYS OF KING ARTHUR

BY Harold R Foster

Synopsis: YOUNG GEOFFREY SITS IN HIS CELL, A LONELY, FRIGHTENED BOY CHARGED WITH SUCH CRIMES AS DESERTION, HORSE STEALING AND RESISTING ARREST!

AND SIR BALDWIN SEEKS AUDIENCE WITH THE KING. "SIRE, THIS DAY ONE OF MY SQUIRES WILL STAND BEFORE YOU TO BE JUDGED, AND HIS CRIMES ARE SERIOUS!"

"BUT, OF ALL THE LADS IN MY CHARGE, NONE IS MORE WORTHY OF KNIGHTHOOD! WITHOUT HESITATION HE HAS SACRIFICED ALL IN THE SERVICE OF OTHERS!"

THE KING LISTENS BUT SAYS NOTHING. LATER HE MAKES CERTAIN ARRANGEMENTS.

A FORLORN FIGURE STANDS BEFORE HIS KING, AND ABOUT THEM ARE GROUPED THE SPLENDID KNIGHTS OF THE ROUND TABLE. GEOFF HOLDS BACK THE TEARS — FOR NOW ALL HOPE OF EVER BEING ONE OF THAT GLITTERING COMPANY IS GONE!

THEN THE KING PASSES SENTENCE. "YOU ARE TO BE BANISHED FROM OUR KINGDOM FOR A YEAR AND A DAY!"

OUTCAST! TO ROAM A HOMELESS WORLD A VAGABOND! SO STUNNED IS HE THAT HE DOES NOT NOTICE WHO IS LEADING HIM AWAY.

HE IS IN A BARGE HEADED FOR THE SEA BEFORE HE FULLY REALIZES HE IS WITH THE COMPANY BOUND FOR NEWCASTLE TO JOIN PRINCE VALIANT AND ALETA!

NEXT WEEK— The Outcast.

Prince Valiant
IN THE DAYS OF KING ARTHUR
BY Harold R. Foster

Synopsis: FOR STEALING THE KING'S HORSES GEOFF IS BANISHED FROM THE KINGDOM FOR A YEAR AND A DAY, TO WANDER PENNILESS, HOMELESS IN FOREIGN LANDS! HE IS PLACED ABOARD A BARGE ALONG WITH OTHER TRAVELERS AND ROWED TO THE SEA.

IT IS NOT UNTIL THEY ALL BOARD THE SAME VESSEL THAT THE WONDERFUL TRUTH DAWNS ON HIM; THAT HE IS GOING TO NEWCASTLE, TOO, AND WILL ONCE AGAIN BE WITH ALETA AND PRINCE VALIANT!

KATWIN SEES THE PUZZLED LOOK ON HIS FACE. "THE KING IS A GREAT-HEARTED GENTLEMAN," SHE SAYS, "AND HE REMEMBERED THAT HE TOO WAS A TROUBLESOME LAD ONCE!"

SO THEY LEAVE THE CALM WATERS OF THE SOLENT AND SAIL UP THE WINDY CHANNEL TOWARD THE NORTH SEA.

AND THE NORTH SEA IS UNKIND TO A LAD WHO HAS NEVER SAILED BEFORE.

THEY ENTER THE CALM REACHES OF THE TYNE RIVER AND BOTH THE SHIP AND GEOFF'S STOMACH CEASE ROCKING.

AS THE ANCHOR IS DROPPED AT NEWCASTLE, THE FIRST TO GREET THEM IS ALETA, ANXIOUS TO HOLD HER SMALL SON ONCE MORE IN HER ARMS.

SOMEWHERE IN THE TOWN THERE IS A HAPPY REUNION WITH MUCH GAY LAUGHTER, BUT GEOFFREY IS NOT A PART OF IT. AS AN EXILE, HE CANNOT SET FOOT ON BRITAIN'S SOIL.

NEXT WEEK - *Boltar's Return*.

Prince Valiant
IN THE DAYS OF KING ARTHUR
by Harold R Foster

Synopsis: PRINCE ARN:—"OFTEN HAS MY SIRE RETURNED FROM DOING MAN'S WORK AND RECEIVED A GREAT WELCOME. NOW IT IS MY TURN, FOR I HAVE TRAVELED FAR AND SAILED WIDE SEAS, AND I MAKE EVERY-ONE HAPPY WHEN I ARRIVE!"

"BUT I SAVE MY BIG SURPRISE FOR THE RIGHT MOMENT! THEN I GRIN AND SHOW IT AND THEY SCREAM WITH DELIGHT. FOR I REALLY BELIEVE IT'S THE MOST WONDERFUL TOOTH IN THE WORLD!"

LONELY AND FORGOTTEN, UNABLE TO GO ASHORE BECAUSE HE HAS BEEN BANISHED BY THE KING, GEOFFREY CAN ONLY WAIT.

THEN TRAGEDY STRIKES AGAIN! A MERCHANT COMES TO CHARTER THE SHIP AND STRIKES A BARGAIN WITH THE CAPTAIN. SOON THE VESSEL IS LOADED AND READY TO SAIL.

THE CAPTAIN IS A HARD MAN BUT FAIR. — "IF YOU CAN'T LAND ON BRITAIN'S SOIL, I'LL PUT YOU ASHORE AT THE BORDER, ONLY A FEW MILES FROM HERE."

WHERE THE EASTERN END OF HADRIAN'S WALL MEETS THE SEA THERE IS THE VIL-LAGE OF WALLSEND AND HERE GEOFF IS PUT ASHORE.

A ROWDY, VIOLENT TOWN OF OUTLAWS AND PIRATES, WHO CAN STEP ACROSS THE BORDER WHEN THE KING'S MEN APPROACH.

GEOFF IS SEEKING LODGINGS WHEN THE DOOR BURSTS OPEN AND AN UNFORGETTABLE VOICE ROARS: "BROACH A CASK OF WINE, LANDLORD. BOLTAR IS THIRSTY!"

NEXT WEEK—**An Old Comrade.**

671   12-18-49

Prince Valiant
IN THE DAYS OF KING ARTHUR
BY Harold R Foster

Synopsis : BOLTAR ORDERS A CASK OF WINE AND SETS ABOUT QUENCHING HIS FAMOUS THIRST. THEN HE NOTICES THE LAD HE HAD SENT SPRAWLING BY HIS BOISTEROUS ENTRY.

AND BOLTAR LAUGHS AT GEOFFREY, FOR IT IS INDEED STRANGE TO SEE A MERE BOY DRESSED IN SHIRT OF MAIL AND CARRYING SHIELD AND SWORD.

" I CRAVE PARDON, SIR BOY ! " SAYS BOLTAR WITH CLUMSY GOOD HUMOR . " BUT DID I SPILL YOUR CRADLE UPON ENTERING ? AND HOW GOES THE BATTLE IN THE NURSERY ? "

" I AM NOT A BOY ! " SNAPS GEOFFREY, HOTLY. " I MEAN I AM A FIGHTING MAN ! WHY, I HAVE FOUGHT THE PICTS SIDE BY SIDE WITH PRINCE VALIANT ! "

" PRINCE VALIANT ! DID YOU SAY PRINCE VAL-IANT ? THE TALL LAD WITH THE LIGHT HEART AND THE AWFUL SWORD ? HE SAILED WITH ME TO AFRICA AND FOUND MUCH GOLD BUT GAVE IT AWAY TO RANSOM HIS FRIEND SIR GAWAIN ! "

" COME, BOY, LEAD ME TO HIM ! THERE NEVER WAS SUCH A LAD. HE COULD DRINK LIKE A MAN, FIGHT LIKE A DEMON AND SING LIKE AN ANGEL ! "

" AND HE GAVE GOLD AWAY," SAYS BOLTAR IN A HUSHED VOICE, FOR HE WOULD NEVER BE GUILTY OF SUCH EXTRAVAGANCE. " JUST FOR THE SAKE OF FRIENDSHIP ! "

" WHERE IS HE, BOY ? " " HE LIES WOUNDED IN NEWCASTLE, JUST A FEW MILES UP THE TYNE . I CANNOT GO WITH YOU, FOR THE KING HAS BANISHED ME FROM BRITAIN ."

672 12 — 25 - 49

" BUT GIVE HIM MY GREETINGS," AND GEOFF'S VOICE TREMBLES, " AND TELL HIM I'LL BE HERE...WAITING."

NEXT WEEK - A Message to ARF.

HAL FOSTER

Prince Valiant
IN THE DAYS OF KING ARTHUR
BY Harold R. Foster

Synopsis: "BUT, BOLTAR, I CANNOT LEAD YOU TO PRINCE VALIANT," GEOFF SAYS. "I HAVE BEEN BANISHED BY MY KING AND MUST NOT TREAD ON BRITAIN'S SOIL!"

BUT A THUNDERING ROAR FROM BOLTAR BRINGS SOME OF HIS MEN WITH SACKS WHICH THEY FILL WITH CALEDONIAN SOIL AND GEOFFREY'S FEET.

THEN THEY BOARD SHIP AND PULL UP THE TYNE TO NEWCASTLE. IT IS HARD WORK AND THEY MUST MOISTEN PARCHED LIPS OFTEN FROM BOLTAR'S CASK.

GEOFF NEVER SETS FOOT TO BRITAIN'S SOIL, BUT, SOMEHOW, HE WONDERS IF DISOBEDIENCE WOULD NOT HAVE BEEN MUCH MORE COMFORTABLE.

VAL LISTENS TO THE APPROACHING NOISE AND HIS FACE IS ALIGHT WITH PLEASURE. "PREPARE ALL THE FOOD IN THE HOUSE, BRING OUT ALL THE WINE...... THEN STAND BACK, FOR WE ARE ABOUT TO HAVE A VISITOR!"

BOLTAR KNOCKS ON THE DOOR AND IT OPENS. "VAL, MY FRIEND!" HE ROARS, "SHED TEARS OF GLADNESS. BOLTAR IS HERE!"

GEOFF IS LUGGED IN, DROPPED, AND THE SAILORS DEPART, FOR THERE IS MORE CHANCE OF A NICE FIGHT AT THE TAVERN THAN HERE.

HE STRUGGLES UPRIGHT, FOR THE MOMENT UNNOTICED IN THE DIN OF BOLTAR'S GREETINGS. THEN HE IS STARTLED BY A FAMILIAR VOICE:- "ARF! ARF, MY BOY! MY SEARCH IS ENDED! I HAVE FOUND YOU!"

COPR. 1949, KING FEATURES SYNDICATE, Inc., WORLD RIGHTS RESERVED   673 1-1-50

HAL FOSTER

"COME HOME WITH ME....... THAT AWFUL WOMAN IS GONE!"

NEXT WEEK - Tor Lay Offers a Haven.

673

Prince Valiant
IN THE DAYS OF KING ARTHUR
BY HAROLD R FOSTER

Synopsis: YOUNG GEOFFREY IS THE ONLY ONE WHO CAN GUIDE THE NOISY BOLTAR TO HIS OLD SHIPMATE, PRINCE VALIANT; BUT GEOFF IS FORBIDDEN TO SET FOOT ON BRITAIN'S SOIL ... SO BOLTAR FILLS TWO SACKS WITH THE SOIL OF CALEDONIA, AND THE MEETING TAKES PLACE.

THE RIOTOUS GREETINGS ARE FURTHER COMPLICATED BY A STRANGE VOICE CRYING: *"ARF, ARF, MY BOY, THAT AWFUL WOMAN IS GONE. YOU ARE FREE TO COME HOME!"*

BOLTAR IS NOT PLEASED WITH THE INTERRUPTION. *"ARF, ARF!"* HE MOCKS, *"IS IT A DOG BARKING? TAKE YOUR NOISE TO THE KENNELS!"*

"DO NOT JEST," ANSWERS THE STRANGER, *"FOR I BRING GOOD TIDINGS TO MASTER ARF, SON OF SIR HUGO GEOFFREY, WHO WAS DRIVEN FROM HOME BY A CRUEL STEPMOTHER."*

"SHE WAS YOUNG AND FAIR OF FACE BUT SELF-WILLED AND SELFISH AT HEART. SHE COULD NOT ABIDE SHARING SIR HUGO'S LOVE WITH HIS SON."

"SHE CAUSED ARF TO RUN AWAY FROM HOME. A FEW MONTHS LATER SHE WAS PROVED AN UNFAITHFUL WIFE. GALLANT SIR HUGO WISHED TO PRESENT HER WITH A HEMPEN NECKLACE BUT SHE DISAPPEARED!"

GEOFF, OR RATHER ARF, FEELS A GLOW OF HAPPINESS. HE IS, AFTER ALL, LITTLE MORE THAN A CHILD AND HOME IS A PRECIOUS PLACE NOW THAT THAT WOMAN CAN NO LONGER TROUBLE HIM.

THEN HE LOOKS AT THE LADY ALETA TO WHOM HE HAS GIVEN HIS HEART; AT PRINCE VALIANT, HIS HERO, HIS FRIEND. HE SWALLOWS HARD, FOR HE HAS A DECISION TO MAKE.

NEXT WEEK — Arf's Decision.

674   1—8—50   HAL FOSTER

Prince Valiant
IN THE DAYS OF KING ARTHUR
BY HAROLD R. FOSTER

Synopsis: ALL EYES ARE TURNED TO YOUNG GEOFFREY AS THEY AWAIT HIS EXPLANATION. THIS IS HIS GREAT MOMENT. HE IS THE CENTER OF ATTENTION, THE MAN OF MYSTERY! HE PAUSES DRAMATICALLY:—"MY NAME IS INDEED ARF GEOFFREY......!"

".....BUT WHEN THAT WOMAN CAUSED ME TO LEAVE HOME I TOOK THE NAME OF 'GEOFFREY ARF,' DETERMINED NEVER TO RETURN UNTIL I HAD BECOME SIR GEOFFREY, KNIGHT OF THE ROUND TABLE!"

TOR LAY GETS INTO THE ACT: "THAT UNFAITHFUL WOMAN IS GONE NOW. WILL YOU RETURN WITH ME TO YOUR FATHER?"

ARF IS VERY YOUNG, VERY SERIOUS. "NO!" HE DECLAIMS, "I REMAIN TO FIGHT SIDE BY SIDE WITH SIR VALIANT AND TO RENDER SERVICE TO MY LADY ALETA AS LONG AS LIFE LASTS!" HE THROWS UP HIS ARM IN A NOBLE GESTURE.......

.... AND FALLS FLAT. HE HAS FORGOTTEN THAT, SINCE HIS EXILE FROM BRITAIN, HE HAS BEEN STANDING IN FOREIGN SOIL! THE TENSION OF DRAMA IS BROKEN BY THE RELIEF OF COMEDY.

BUT, BEFORE LAUGHTER CAN COME TO EMBARRASS ARF, BOLTAR BANGS HIS NOW EMPTY KEG ON THE TABLE. "WELL SAID, LAD!" HE BOOMS, "NOW LET US EAT AND DRINK, FOR EMOTIONAL SCENES ALWAYS MAKE A SENSITIVE MAN HUNGRY!"

ON THE MORROW THEY ARE TO SAIL FOR THULE, SO TONIGHT CELLAR AND CUPBOARD ARE SWEPT BARE IN AN EFFORT TO SATISFY THE CELEBRATED APPETITE OF BOLTAR.

NEXT WEEK:— The Anxious Parent.

HAL FOSTER

Prince Valiant
IN THE DAYS OF KING ARTHUR
BY HAROLD R FOSTER

Synopsis: TOR LAY IS ABOUT TO LEAVE FOR THE DULL AND LONELY CASTLE OF HIS MASTER. HE LOOKS AROUND. SIR VALIANT AND HIS LOVELY WIFE SEEM WEALTHY, THEY LIVE WITH LOVE AND LAUGHTER, GOOD FOOD, GOOD WINE. HE MAKES A DECISION.

"I WILL GO WITH YOU," HE ANNOUNCES. "IT IS MY DUTY TO BE WITH MASTER ARF, TO CARE FOR, INSTRUCT AND ADVISE HIM !"

ALETA GUIDES THE OLD HUMBUG TO THE DOOR AND HANDS HIM HIS TRAVELING BAG. "YOU WILL DO NOTHING OF THE SORT !" SHE SCOLDS.

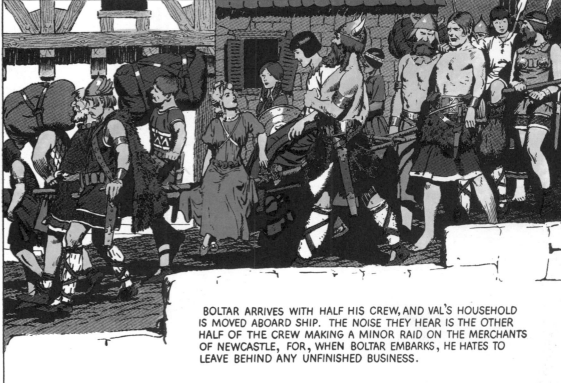

"HIS POOR FATHER MUST BE NIGH WILD WITH ANXIETY, NOT KNOWING WHETHER HIS MISSING SON IS DEAD OR ALIVE ! GO STRAIGHTWAY AND TELL HIM I WILL CARE FOR ARF AS IF HE WERE MY YOUNGER BROTHER. HE WILL RETURN HOME WHEN HIS YEAR OF EXILE IS OVER !"

BOLTAR ARRIVES WITH HALF HIS CREW, AND VAL'S HOUSEHOLD IS MOVED ABOARD SHIP. THE NOISE THEY HEAR IS THE OTHER HALF OF THE CREW MAKING A MINOR RAID ON THE MERCHANTS OF NEWCASTLE, FOR, WHEN BOLTAR EMBARKS, HE HATES TO LEAVE BEHIND ANY UNFINISHED BUSINESS.

BOLTAR'S TIMING IS PERFECT ! HARDLY HAVE THEY EMBARKED WHEN THE REST OF THE CREW ARRIVES, HEAVILY LADEN WITH THE MERCHANDISE THEY HAVE BORROWED, AND HOTLY PURSUED BY THE LOCAL SOLDIERY.

676   1-22-50

A FEW ARROWS COME ABOARD, BUT SOON THEY ARE FAR FROM SHORE AND THE VOYAGE TO THULE IS BEGUN.

NEXT WEEK : A Business Deal.

Prince Valiant
IN THE DAYS OF KING ARTHUR
BY HAROLD R FOSTER

Synopsis: THE LONG DRAGON-SHIP GLIDES SWIFTLY SEA-WARD AND THE TWO ARMED SHIPS THAT FOLLOW ARE LEFT BEHIND. BOLTAR SIGHS, FOR THE MERCHANTS OF ANY TOWN HE VISITS ALWAYS SEEM SO UNFRIENDLY WHEN HE LEAVES. THEN HE ORDERS A SHELTER CONSTRUCTED FOR HIS NOBLE PASSENGERS.

THEY TURN NORTHWARD UP THE ROCKY COAST OF CALEDONIA. THE GREAT SAIL IS FURLED AND OARSMEN BEND TO THE SWEEPS FOR THE WINDS ARE UNFAVORABLE.

DAYS PASS, STORMS BUFFET THEM, RAIN AND FOG OBSCURE THE LAND.

THERE ARE ALSO DAYS, SUNNY AND CRISP WITH THE APPROACH OF WINTER, THAT BRING BACK VAL'S STRENGTH AND HE CAN EXERCISE HIS STIFFENED MUSCLES.

YOUNG ARF CRAWLS FROM HIS QUARTERS, PALE AND SHAKY BUT, FOR THE FIRST TIME SINCE LEAVING LAND, HE BELIEVES HE WILL LIVE.

COMES A DAY WHEN WINDS ARE FAVORABLE. THE SAIL IS SET AND THE OARS RACKED. THEN THE MEN PUT THEIR GEAR IN ORDER AND CAREFULLY SHARPEN THEIR SWORDS.

VAL IS SUSPICIOUS OF THIS ACTIVITY. "CAN IT BE THAT YOU PLAN TO RISK OUR NECKS ON SOME PLUNDERING RAID?" HE ASKS.

COPR. 1950, KING FEATURES SYNDICATE, Inc., WORLD RIGHTS RESERVED.   677 1-29-50

" I WILL HAVE YOU KNOW, SIR VALIANT, THAT I AM A RESPECTABLE BUSINESSMAN ! " SNAPS BOLTAR WITH GREAT DIGNITY. " I PLAN NO-THING MORE THAN ONE MORE BUSINESS DEAL BEFORE CROSSING THE SEAS TO THULE ! "

Hal Foster

NEXT WEEK — That Business Deal.

677

Prince Valiant
IN THE DAYS OF KING ARTHUR
BY Harold R Foster

Synopsis: "YOU HAVE HURT ME DEEPLY, SIR VALIANT, BY HINTING THAT I AM ABOUT TO MAKE A THIEVING RAID!" SAYS THE SENSITIVE BOLTAR AS HE PUTS A NICE EDGE ON HIS AXE. "I MERELY PLAN A LITTLE BUSINESS TRANSACTION."

LATE IN THE DAY THEY PASS A HARBOR ENTRANCE AND SEE WITHIN ITS SHELTER A PROSPEROUS CITY. BOLTAR SAILS ON GRUMBLING: "MY MEN NEED EXERCISE. TOO LONG HAVE THEY BEEN ON SHIPBOARD."

SO, A MILE BEYOND THE TOWN, HE SENDS ALL BUT A FEW ASHORE IN THE GATHERING DUSK.

AND THESE MEN OBEY THEIR CHIEFTAIN BY RUNNING. THEY RUN SWIFTLY NOR DO THEY STOP WHEN THEY REACH THE TOWN, BUT RUN RIGHT THROUGH UNTIL THEY COME TO THE QUARTER WHERE STAND THE WAREHOUSES OF THE MERCHANTS.

BOLTAR'S SHIP COMES SLOWLY INTO THE HARBOR, UNCHALLENGED. FOR SOMETHING SEEMS TO HAVE HAPPENED TO THE SENTRY IN THE DARKNESS.

AS THE SHIP GLIDES SILENTLY ALONGSIDE THE QUAY THERE IS A GROWING TUMULT WITHIN THE CITY. THE SOUND OF AXES ON STOUT DOORS CAN BE PLAINLY HEARD!

PRINCE VALIANT BIDS ALETA STAY WITHIN THE SHELTER OF THEIR CABIN AND STEPS ON DECK FULLY ARMED SAVE FOR HIS SHIELD, FOR HIS LEFT SIDE IS STILL WEAK FROM THE WOUND.

COPR. 1950, KING FEATURES SYNDICATE, Inc. WORLD RIGHTS RESERVED   678   2-5-50

"NOISY TOWN, ISN'T IT?" REMARKS BOLTAR VIRTUOUSLY. "ITS CITIZENS MUST BE ROISTERING IN THE TAVERNS!"

NEXT WEEK - The Unfriendly City

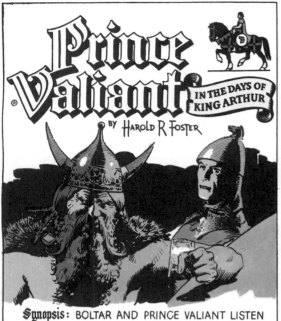

Prince Valiant
IN THE DAYS OF KING ARTHUR
BY HAROLD R. FOSTER

Synopsis: BOLTAR AND PRINCE VALIANT LISTEN TO THE GROWING TUMULT WITHIN THE CITY. "I NEVER SHOULD HAVE ALLOWED MY POOR, INNOCENT BOYS TO GO INTO THAT NOISY TOWN!" MUTTERS THEIR CAPTAIN PIOUSLY. "ITS CITIZENS SEEM MOST UNFRIENDLY."

A LANTERN IS HOISTED TO THE YARD TO GUIDE THE SAILORS THOUGH THERE IS PLENTY OF LIGHT, FOR A WAREHOUSE SEEMS TO BE BURNING.

THEN SOME OF THE POOR, INNOCENT 'BOYS' CAN BE SEEN RETURNING, BENDING BENEATH THE WEIGHT OF BOXES AND BALES.

THESE ARE TOSSED ABOARD AND THE 'BOYS' RETURN FOR MORE. BOLTAR TURNS TO VAL. "THE LADS MUST HAVE MADE SOME PURCHASES," HE EXPLAINS.

FINALLY THE WHOLE CREW RETURNS, BACKING SLOWLY TOWARD THE SHIP AMID A SHOWER OF MISSILES. THEN, AS THE VESSEL MOVES AWAY FROM THE QUAY, THEY TURN QUICKLY AND LEAP ABOARD!

BY DAWN THE 'PURCHASES' ARE ALL STOWED, THE MOUNTAINS OF CALEDONIA ARE FAINT IN THE DISTANCE AND AHEAD THE WIDE, WILD EMPTY SEA.

679 2-12-50

THE PASSENGERS COME OUT ON THE SUNNY DECK AND, AS USUAL, THE SIGHT OF KATWIN SETS BOLTAR STRUTTING LIKE A ROOSTER.

BUT TILLICUM HANDS PRINCE ARN TO KATWIN, WALKS UP TO BOLTAR AND SAYS VERY QUIETLY: "ENDANGER THE SUN-WOMAN'S MAN-CHILD AGAIN AND I WILL KILL YOU."
NEXT WEEK – Out to Sea.

Prince Valiant

IN THE DAYS OF KING ARTHUR

BY HAROLD R. FOSTER

Synopsis: BOLTAR IS QUITE PLEASED WITH HIS PROFITABLE RAID UNTIL THAT STRANGE, DARK WOMAN NAMED TILLICUM TELLS HIM: "IF, ONCE AGAIN, YOU ENDANGER THE LIFE OF THE SUN-WOMAN'S MAN-CHILD, I WILL KILL YOU."

THEN SHE SITS DOWN AND PRINCE ARN CRAWLS INTO HER LAP, AND BOLTAR PULLS ANGRILY ON HIS BEARD. A SCORE OF TIMES HE HAS LAUGHED IN THE FACE OF SUCH THREATS FROM HARDY WARRIORS AND GREAT CHIEFTAINS . . . . . .

. . . . . BUT THIS QUIET WOMAN HASN'T THREATENED; SHE HAS SIMPLY STATED A FACT, AND COLD SHIVERS RUN THROUGH HIS GREAT BODY.

BOLTAR IS A PATRIOTIC MAN. "I REALLY OWE IT TO MY KING TO BRING PRINCE VALIANT, THE QUEEN ALETA AND THEIR YOUNG SON SAFELY ACROSS THE SEAS TO THULE," HE REASONS AS THE DRAGON-SHIP PASSES A RICH MERCHANT VESSEL, TO THE SURPRISE OF ITS CREW AND THE DESPAIR OF HIS OWN!

FOR SEVERAL DAYS THEY SAIL IN WEATHER FAIR AND FOUL AND, AT LAST, REACH THE ORKNEY ISLANDS AND THE SHELTER OF SCAPA FLOW.

HERE THEY TAKE ON WOOD AND WATER, FOR AHEAD OF THEM LIES A LONG AND PERILOUS JOURNEY. WITHOUT SEXTANT OR COMPASS, IN SPITE OF WINDS OR CURRENT, A TRACKLESS WASTE OF SEA MUST BE TRAVELED.

680 2-19-50

YOUNG ARF IS WIDE-EYED WITH AWE AS SEA AND SKY UNFOLD THEIR WONDERS. HE BEHOLDS THE GREAT FALL MIGRATION OF WATERFOWL, WHILE FROM THE SEA HUGE MONSTERS LEAP!

A SHARP COMMAND FROM VAL ENDS THE HOLIDAY AND ARF GOES TO WORK . . . . FOR KNIGHTHOOD COMES ONLY TO THE BEST.

NEXT WEEK - The Perils of the Sea.

Prince Valiant

IN THE DAYS OF KING ARTHUR

BY HAROLD R FOSTER

Synopsis: THE ISLANDS OF ORKNEY FALL BEHIND AND FOR DAYS AND DAYS NOTHING IS TO BE SEEN BUT THE RAGGED, WINDY SKY AND THE GRAY SEA.

THE MENACE OF SHRIEKING WINDS AND HISSING WAVES IS FORGOTTEN AS MONSTERS OF THE DEEP GO SURGING BY-- MONSTERS SO HUGE THEY PAY NO HEED TO THE FRAIL DRAGON-SHIP.

WITH NEITHER COMPASS NOR SEXTANT BUT ONLY BOLTAR'S SKILL THEY FIND THEIR WAY ACROSS THE EMPTY WASTE OF SEA TO THE SHETLAND ISLANDS.

IN A SHELTERED COVE THEY REST AND PUT THEIR GEAR IN ORDER, FOR THE WORST IS STILL AHEAD.

WHITE FLAKES HERALD THE APPROACH OF WINTER AND, FOR THE SECOND TIME IN HIS SHORT BUT EVENTFUL LIFE, PRINCE ARN SEES SNOW !

THEN ONCE AGAIN THEY PUT TO SEA, SAILING NORTH BY EAST UNTIL THE NORTH STAR SEEMS ALMOST OVERHEAD. ICE CRUSTS THE SHROUDS AND THE NORTHERN LIGHTS FLAME IN THE SKY !

AFTER ENDLESS DAYS THEY SEE THE TOWERING COASTS OF THULE STANDING AGLOW IN THE DAWN LIGHT. HOMELAND !

INTO A QUIET FJORD GLIDES THE DRAGON-SHIP. THE PERILOUS SEA VOYAGE IS ENDED AND THE WARMTH AND COMFORT OF A VILLAGE INN IS THEIRS.

NEXT WEEK- *Journey's End.*

HAL FOSTER

Prince Valiant
IN THE DAYS OF KING ARTHUR
BY Harold R. Foster

Synopsis: PRINCE VALIANT AND HIS PARTY REST FROM THE HARDSHIPS OF THEIR LONG SEA VOYAGE, WHILE A MESSENGER IS SENT OVER THE HILLS TO THE KING OF THULE.

IN HIS GREAT HALL THE LONELY KING HEARS THE MESSENGER TELL OF HIS SON'S RETURNING AND HIS EYES GROW MISTY.

"I MUST ARRANGE A HUNT SO MY SON AND I MAY ONCE AGAIN RIDE SIDE BY SIDE! AND YOUNG PEOPLE MUST BE INVITED TO COME AND STAY. A BANQUET! I MUST HAVE HIS ROOMS PREPARED......!"

".....AND ALETA WILL COME TOO, TO UPSET MY QUIET WITH HER LAUGHTER AND SILLY SONGS, TO MEDDLE IN AFFAIRS OF STATE AND TO TEASE ME LIKE A MISCHIEVOUS SMALL SUNBEAM!"

AGUAR, KING OF THULE, LETS OUT A ROAR THAT BRINGS HIS STAFF ON THE RUN: – "CLEAN UP THIS UNSIGHTLY STABLE! WASH DOWN THE WALLS! SCRUB THE FLOORS! POLISH THE FURNITURE! HANG FRESH TAPESTRIES! SHINE UP THIS OLD BARRACKS UNTIL IT IS FIT FOR THE FUTURE QUEEN OF THULE!"

DOWN BY THE SEA OLD FRIENDS BID FAREWELL. THERE IS MUCH LAUGHING AND LOUD TALK TO HIDE THE SORROW OF PARTING.

TILLICUM SITS QUIETLY APART, HER FIERCE EYES FIXED ON THE MAN WHOSE LIFE SHE HAD THREATENED, WHOSE RAID SHE HAD FORBIDDEN. BOLTAR STRIDES TOWARD HER....

...AND FROM HIS NECK TAKES A HEAVY GOLDEN CHAIN AND DROPS IT IN HER LAP: – "I WILL RETURN!," HE WHISPERS.

MANY RIGHTEOUS PEOPLE WILL NOT APPROVE OF BOLTAR, THE PIRATE. BUT HE LIVED IN THE BOISTEROUS DAYS WHEN THE RAIDER WAS LOOKED UPON AS A RESPECTABLE BUSINESSMAN WHO MADE HIS PROFITS BY RISKING HIS LIFE RATHER THAN BY SHREWD TRADING.
NEXT WEEK– Home Again.

Synopsis: THE HORSES ARRIVE AND PRINCE VALIANT AND HIS FAMILY SET OUT ACROSS THE RUGGED HILLS. TILLICUM HAS NEVER BEEN ON A HORSE NOR WILL SHE TRUST PRINCE ARN TO ONE. INDIAN FASHION SHE GOES AND HER HEART IS SINGING, FOR THE FOREST-CLAD HILLS OF THULE ARE JUST LIKE HER HOMELAND ACROSS THE WIDE SEAS.

KING AGUAR HEARS THE SHOUTS OF WELCOME, HIS SON'S RINGING VOICE IN GREETING AND THE RIPPLE OF ALETA'S LAUGHTER.

HIS VISION BECOMES BLURRED AND HE MUST BLOW HIS NOSE VIOLENTLY. ALREADY THE GRIM OLD CASTLE SEEMS TO HAVE BECOME WARMER, BRIGHTER!

VAL BOWS POLITELY: "I TRUST YOU HAVE BEEN WELL, SIRE?" THE KING ALSO BOWS: "SPLENDID," HE ANSWERS—"AND WILL YOU BE STAYING FOR SUPPER?"

WE PASS LIGHTLY OVER THE NEXT SCENE BECAUSE IT IS INCLINED TO BE EMOTIONAL. SUFFICE IT TO SAY THAT AGUAR IS A WISE AND JUST KING BECAUSE HE DESIRES TO BE WORTHY OF HIS STALWART SON, AND VAL IS A GREAT WARRIOR FOR HE COPIES HIS BELOVED FATHER IN EVERYTHING.)

FROM BEYOND THE CURTAINED DOORWAY COMES A BEDLAM OF NOISE, SCREAMS, BELLOWS, SHRIEKS AND SOBS — BAD-TEMPERED, DEMANDING! "WHAT IN THUNDER IS THAT?" CRIES THE KING IN ALARM!

IT IS ONLY PRINCE ARN ASKING FOR HIS MOTHER. VAL AND ALETA WERE PLANNING TO SURPRISE THE KING—NO DOUBT THEY DID!

NEXT WEEK— "My Sword"

683

Prince Valiant
IN THE DAYS OF KING ARTHUR
BY HAROLD R FOSTER

Synopsis: "VERY SOON NOW, I WILL BE A MAN; FOR TODAY I HAVE YET ANOTHER TOOTH! MOMMIE SQUEALS FOR JOY AND MUST SHOW IT TO EVERYONE. I GET VERY TIRED OF HAVING MY MOUTH PRIED OPEN....I WISH MOMMIE WOULD GROW UP!"

"I SHOULD HAVE A SWORD OF MY OWN NOW; I AM BIG ENOUGH.. ALMOST. ONE LIKE MY SIRE CARRIES AS HE GOES SHOUTING INTO BATTLE....THERE IT HANGS, GLEAMING, ON THE WALL."

"THERE ARE BRIGHT THINGS ON THE HILT– BRIGHTER THAN MY SIRE'S TEETH WHEN HE LAUGHS. BRIGHT AS MOMMIE'S EYES WHEN SHE SMILES DOWN AT ME!"

"MY SIRE'S SWORD WILL BE MINE SOME DAY. IT IS VERY FAR AWAY BUT I AM DETERMINED TO TRY FOR IT."

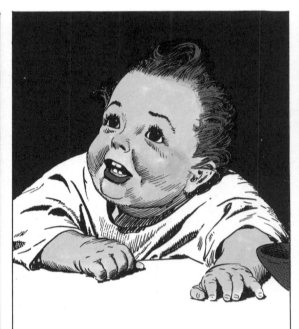

"I GUESS I MUST HAVE CLIMBED A MILLION MILES....AND FALLEN A HUNDRED TIMES!"

"BUT A QUEST IS A QUEST AND MUST BE CARRIED THROUGH, SO AT LAST I REACH OUR SWORD."

"I REALLY DON'T KNOW WHAT HAPPENED, BUT ONCE MY GOOD RIGHT HAND HAD GRASPED THE HILT NOTHING COULD BREAK ITS GRIP ON MY SWORD."

"I DIDN'T KNOW WHAT TO DO WITH IT SO I TASTED IT, AND THE HILT WAS ALL SALTY FROM THE SWEAT OF MY SIRE'S STRONG HAND WHERE HE GRIPPED IT IN MANY A FIGHT."

684   3-19-50

HAL FOSTER

"THEN, THOSE WHO SERVE ME GATHERED AROUND AND MADE MUCH ADO OVER MY LUMPS, BUT TILLICUM AND MY SIRE LOOKED AT MY ACHIEVEMENT AND WERE PROUD. I AM INDEED A MAN! WELL, ALMOST.....FOR MOMMIE'S ARMS STILL FEEL WARM AND COMFORTING AND SHE SMELLS SO SWEET.... BETTER THAN ANY OLD WAR HORSE, I'LL WAGER!"

NEXT WEEK – The Stolen Kiss.